My Colourful Day!

how many colours can *you* see?

Text and illustrations copyright © Merida Woodford, 1993

The moral right of the author/illustrator has been asserted

First published in Great Britain 1993 by Blackie Children's Books

This edition first published 1995 by Happy Cat Books, Bradfield, Essex CO11 2UT

All rights reserved

A CIP catalogue record for this book is available from the British Library

ISBN 1 899248 10 2

Printed in Hong Kong

My Colourful Day!

how many colours can *you* see?

Merida Woodford

Happy Cat Books

When I wake up, the
first thing I see is the
YELLOW sun shining
through my window.

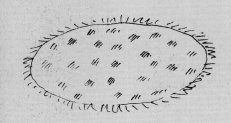

I jump into the PINK
bath and play with my
toy duck.

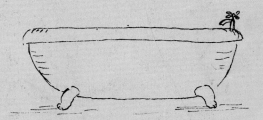

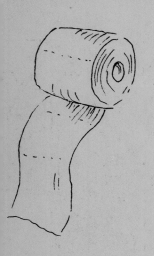

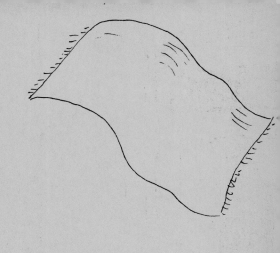

Then I get out and dry myself with a big BLUE towel.

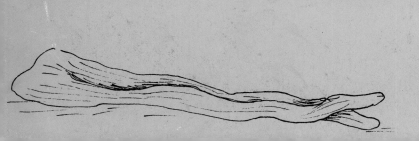

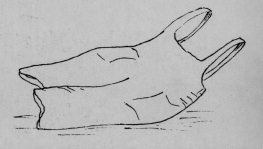

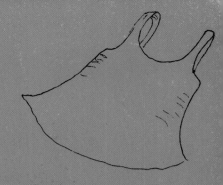

I put on my favourite RED dress and run downstairs.

For breakfast I have some BROWN bread with butter, and a big glass of milk.

Then I put on my
PURPLE coat and
boots, and go outside.

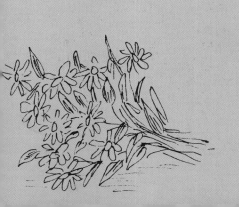
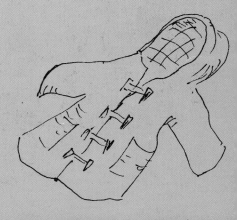

Oh, what fun it is to play in the GREEN fields nearby...

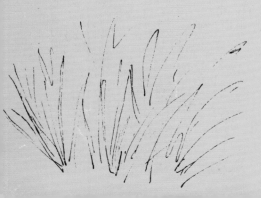

...and to follow the
fluffy WHITE sheep
down the lane.

When the skies turn
GREY and it starts to
rain, I hurry back.

At home, I sit in front of the warm ORANGE fire, listening to my favourite stories.

When it's time for bed,
I look at the BLACK
world outside.

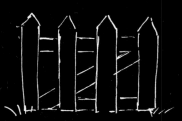

Then I get into
bed and close
my eyes on another
COLOURFUL day.